Taming the Rivers

a riverside walk

CW00408470

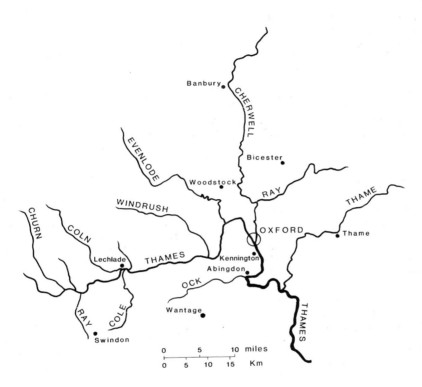

Banbury
CHERWELL
EVENLODE
Bicester
Woodstock
RAY
WINDRUSH
THAME
CHURN
COLN
OXFORD
Thame
Lechlade
THAMES
Kennington
Abingdon
OCK
RAY
COLE
Wantage
THAMES
Swindon

0   5   10 miles
0   5   10   15   Km

Derek M Elsom

Oxford Polytechnic

Oxford Region Thematic Trail No 1

ISBN 0-948444-08-8

Copyright Derek M. Elsom 1987

INTRODUCTION

The rivers and meadows which surround the older parts of Oxford have played an important part in shaping the development of Oxford as well as affecting the lives of the people who live close to the rivers. The presence of a ford across the river Thames ('oxen ford') provided the initial focus of activity which eventually produced the present city. This riverside walk considers some of the links which have developed between the rivers, the people and the city, especially concerning flooding or the threat of flooding. Oxford has a long history of floods and adoption of flood protection measures. At a number of locations along the walk, questions are posed, drawing your attention to the ways in which Oxford is closely linked to its rivers. Although the answers are provided in the booklet, it is hoped you will attempt to answer these questions by interpreting the landscape in front of you. By the end of the walk you may understand better the ways in which the community of Oxford has dealt with, or is dealing with, the flood hazard.

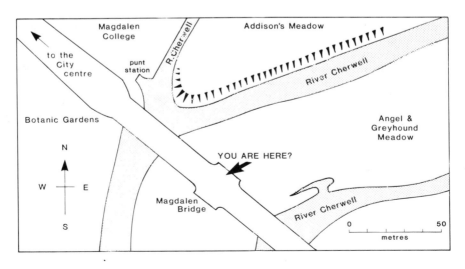

START

From the centre of Oxford, make your way along the High Street, which runs eastwards from the city centre. Stop in the middle of Magdalen Bridge (where the pavement widens and there are some bench seats) on the north (upstream) side. A sketch map is provided to help you.

MAGDALEN BRIDGE

Magdalen Bridge is an impressive location with which to begin this walk. It is overlooked by the splendid Gothic bell tower (1509) of Magdalen College. Across the road from the college lies Britain's first Botanic Garden which was established in 1631. The river here is the Cherwell, and its source lies in northern Oxfordshire near Banbury. There has been a bridge across the river here since the eleventh century, as this is part of the main Oxford-London route. The present classical stone bridge was built in 1772 with some widening at the Magdalen College end being undertaken in 1882-83.

Look north (upstream). In front of you are river channels and extensive lush green grassy areas: the grassy areas are the called 'the meadows'. The nearest is called Angel and Greyhound Meadow and the one beyond the far bank of the river (partly hidden by the raised bank and trees) is called Addison's Meadow (refer to the sketch map). Although they are used as playing fields and recreation grounds or for walks, they are often flooded.

Why should these areas flood frequently?

Causes of flooding

There are two reasons why these grassy areas flood frequently, depending upon whether the causes are thought to be natural or related to the actions taken by the community:

Natural causes: Although the river has cut itself a channel (or several channels) to accommodate the flow of water, the river still overtops its banks once every year or two. Most rivers do this. As the waters spill over the surrounding land fine sediments are deposited producing what is called a floodplain. Most rivers follow a meandering course through their floodplain section.

Actions taken by the community: Just upstream of Magdalen Bridge two river channels of the Cherwell merge (to your left). To your right, another channel passes underneath the bridge and these Cherwell channels merge south of the bridge. At times when the river level is high, the bridge acts as a bottleneck for the river flow. The arches and massive piers of the bridge obstruct the river flow and, if tree branches and other debris become trapped against the piers, the river level quickly builds up behind the bridge.

You may have thought of several other reasons for flooding around Magdalen Bridge, perhaps related to the raising of the bank surrounding Addison's Meadow, or related to the buildings encroaching on the edge of Angel and Greyhound Meadow. However, further discussion of such causes will be left until later in the trail.

An aerial view of Oxford during the floods of March 1947. Magdalen Bridge lies in the left foreground. Many areas can be seen to be flooded including Magdalen College School grounds and Christ Church Meadows.

Walk 150 metres westwards, towards the centre of Oxford, cross the road, and turn left into Rose Lane. Continue to the end of this lane and pass through the large metal gates which lead to Merton Field in front of you. Take the path which bears left and leads you to the riverside. Once you reach the river follow the riverside path for about 200 metres. A bench seat makes a convenient stopping place.

CHRIST CHURCH MEADOWS

From the seat, looking across the river, you can see the Magdalen College School grounds (cricket ground), while behind you is the wide open expanse of Christ Church Meadows. The riverside path on which you are located has been raised by about a metre.

Why should this side of the river be raised and the other side not?

The raised river bank

The simple answer may be that because the river Cherwell floods along this section of its course, the path has been raised to ensure that the path is usable at times of flooding; the other side of the river has no path. An alternative answer could be that the path has been raised to form a river embankment to protect Christ Church Meadows from flooding. The absence of an embankment on the other side of the river suggests either that it is deemed too costly to protect Magdalen College School grounds or that it is deliberately allowed to flood.

These answers are correct to varying degrees. Since the 16th-century the Meadows have been regarded as being within the precincts of Christ Church College, and as a trust to be handed down from generation to generation intact. Indeed, Oxford is very fortunate in having such an unspoilt area of land little more than 100 metres from the city centre. The original path was constructed in the 16th-century from earth that was dug out for Christ Church College buildings and the college paid for the building of this 'raised gravel walk round the Meadows'. The effectiveness of this raised walk as an embankment for flood protection is questionable given that the Meadows have been completely covered with floodwaters many times, most notably in 1809, 1833, 1852, 1882, and as recently as 1947. In December 1852 the Meadows were so badly flooded that it was possible to sail small boats across (as shown in the cover engraving of this booklet). Illustrations of the nineteenth century floods often presented Oxford to the nation as 'a Venice, in its apparent isolation from the land and in the appearance of its towers and spires reflected in the mirror of the floods'.

To sum up, the riverside walk was constructed for the pleasure of walking around Christ Church Meadows, but by successively raising the level of the path it has now become a useful protection against all but the worst floods. However, floodwaters have to go somewhere: it is practically (and economically) impossible to contain all floodwaters within a river channel. If floodwater is stopped from overtopping the river banks along one stretch of the river then that water will add to the floodwaters further downstream, producing deeper and more extensive flooding there. In other words, flooding of a river's natural floodplain must be allowed wherever possible. Even if you are keen on sports, flooding of a playing field in Oxford must be preferable to flooding of streets and houses in say, Kennington or Abingdon, which lie to the south of Oxford!

Continue southwards along the Cherwell towpath. A larger channel of the river Cherwell which has swung around the far side of Magdalen College School grounds merges to produce a much wider channel near the punt-type ferry. Continue on about 300 metres past this ferry until you reach the point where a section of the river splits off to the right, followed by the footpath.

RIVER CHERWELL CHANNEL SPLIT

The narrow shallow channel which bears off to the right, with its slack water, contrasts markedly with the wider deeper channel which continues straight ahead. Yet, only a century ago, this narrow shallow channel was the main channel for the river Cherwell. Compare the sketch maps of 1872 and the present day.

What do you think has happened here?

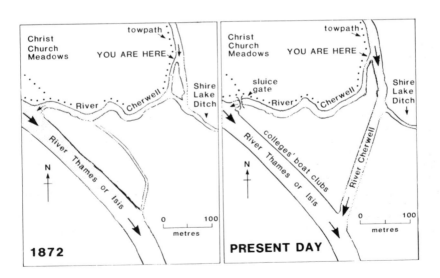

Changes in the channels of the river Cherwell where it joins the Thames.

Construction of the 'new cut'

Over long periods of time rivers change their course naturally, so it is possible that the river cut out the channel which flows straight ahead. However, such a natural change would usually take much longer than a century.

In fact, the straight channel is an artificial one. If you look at the 1872 map, you can see that where the Cherwell joined the Thames, their river flows were opposed to one another. When the Thames was fast-flowing it meant that its waters held up the outflow of the Cherwell. When the Cherwell was held back in this way, ponding of its waters led to extensive flooding of its course for many kilometres upstream as its gradient was only about 1:4000 to 1:8000 (a fall of only one metre in 4 to 8 kilometres). Conversely, on occasions, when the Cherwell was fast-flowing, the Thames was similarly affected. Dr Plot, the 17th-century natural historian, recorded that floodwaters flowed so fast down the Cherwell on 7th May 1663 that when they entered the Thames, the Thames 'was driven back at least a mile', producing an effect like a tidal bore.

Following frequent floods in Oxford, and in many towns along other stretches of the river Thames, in the latter half of the nineteenth century, Parliament set up an Enquiry into Flood Prevention in 1877. One of its recommendations was to straighten and so shorten stretches of the river channel where they caused bottlenecks in the flow of water in flood. Thus in 1884 the 'new cut' was constructed, and it now forms the main channel for the Cherwell entering the Thames. Whereas this channel is now regularly dredged and well-maintained, the old channel has been neglected and left to silt up.

Flooding of Christ Church Meadows, December 1852.

Construction of the 'new cut' in 1884 across the land known as Codger's Island.

Punting on the Thames at the end of Eights Week. Two of the old College barges can be seen in the background.

Continue along the riverside path.

On your right, just before the arched footbridge (1884) which crosses the mouth of the Cherwell and leads to the Oxford University Colleges' Boat Clubs, note the sluice gate from the ditch which drains Christ Church Meadows. This emphasises that the river embankment along which you have been walking for 800 metres may prevent frequent flooding of the Meadows, but should an exceptional flood overflow the embankment (or should the Meadows suffer exceptional rainfall) there needs to be a way of transferring the water back to the river.

Walk to the edge of the river Thames in front of you.

RIVER THAMES

This stretch of the river Thames is known locally as the Isis, presumably, from the latin 'Thamesis'. The famous barges of the Colleges, from which spectators would have had an excellent view of the boat races, were once moored along this stretch of the river. Since the 1930s, these barges have been replaced by college boathouses.

Looking at the river Thames here makes one realise how much more water flows in it compared with the Cherwell. If you wanted to know how much water flows in a river then you would need to measure the width and depth of the river (to obtain the cross-sectional area of the channel) and then multiply this value by the velocity (speed) of the flow of water. The resulting value is called the river's discharge and is usually measured in cubic metres per second (cumecs) or traditionally, million gallons per day.

Suggest how many times greater is the discharge of the river Thames than that of the river Cherwell.

Why should the flow of the water in the Thames be considerably faster than it used to be, say in the last century ?

Estimating river discharge

The discharge of the Thames here exceeds that of the Cherwell by about 8-10 times. If you compare the channel of the Thames here with the Cherwell 'new cut', it is about two to two and a half times as wide and up to twice as deep. Further, the flow of water in the Thames is considerably faster than the Cherwell.

The flow of the river in earlier centuries used to be much slower because there were far more obstructions to, and bottlenecks in, the flow of water. Bridges with narrow arches and wide piers impeded and slowed down the river flow. In order to render the river navigable, the river level has been permanently raised at numerous places along its course by the erection of weirs, with locks alongside to enable boats to pass from one stretch of river to another. Locks and weirs formed impediments to the passage of floodwaters as their sills (bases) were invariably above the natural bed of the river and they reduced the channel width. Mills were commonly established at weirs to utilise the fall of water at these places, and since the miller wished to maintain a good head of water above his mill, he was reluctant to open the weir-sluices to their full extent, even at times of flood. Fish-traps, sometimes placed across the outlets of weirs, frequently became solid obstacles to the passage of water, owing to the weeds, leaves, branches, and floating rubbish which blocked the gaps in the wire netting.

It was not until the Thames Conservancy gained sufficient powers in 1894 to begin to manage the river Thames and its tributaries effectively that the flood problem began to improve. Locks, weirs and bridges have been replaced or removed, circuitous river bends have been straightened, and river channels have been widened and deepened by dredging. All these activities have contributed to a faster flow. The stretch of river in front of you is regularly dredged by the Rivers Division of Thames Water Authority, formed in 1974. A navigable depth of 1.2 metres (4 feet) is maintained along this stretch of the river though the river's depth in places may reach twice this.

This view is taken from the other side of the river and looking upstream towards Folly Bridge. It shows the famous barges of the Colleges moored along the bank. It was taken in 1895 when a coach and six horses were driven onto the frozen Thames. Although winters may be as cold now, the Thames does not freeze as readily because of its faster flow.

Head of the River public house at Folly Bridge. The building was once a warehouse built to store goods in transit to and from London.

Follow the riverside path towards Folly Bridge. The tree-lined avenue of Broad Walk, built on raised land, is on the right. Your path leads you over a small bridge which crosses a minor tributary, known as the Trill Mill Stream, and then to the car park of the Head of the River public house. Walk though the car park, past the Information notice-board (number 4). At the main road turn left to walk across Folly Bridge. Stop halfway across the bridge and look back along the riverside path you have walked.

FOLLY BRIDGE

Although the present Folly Bridge was built between 1825 and 1827, there has probably been a bridge across the Thames here since the 11th-century. The bridge takes its name from a building, used by Friar Bacon (1220-1292) as a study, which once stood on an earlier bridge. The name does not refer to the Victorian brick building with its statues and battlements that stands on the western side of the bridge. It was built in 1849 and is called Caudwell's Castle. A causeway (now the Abingdon Road) provided access to the bridge over the low-lying land on the river floodplain to the south. Folly Bridge provided Oxford with its link to the important centres of Winchester and Southampton.

The river was an important transport route in post-medieval times. As early as 1605 an Oxford-Burcot Commission was established to create an efficient navigation link between Oxford and London. Traders could send the famous Headington stone and other goods to London while Oxford could be supplied with coal, timber, corn, malt and wheat. However, this Commission had only limited powers and it was not very effective in managing the river. Although only Salter Brother's boat-building yards (established 1858) display any river commerce today the general area of Folly Bridge was once a hive of commercial activity. The Head of the River public house was converted in 1975 from an 1830 warehouse to store goods in transit to and from London. One of the original cranes and hoists has been left in front of the public house to remind us of what activity once took place here.

Transporting goods between Oxford and London was dangerous, time-consuming and expensive. Navigation needed weirs to pond back the water to provide sufficient draught for boats along shallow sections of the river. The first weirs constructed in the 17th-century had a central span, about 3-6 metres wide, which could be removed. It was to this central opening that the term 'lock' was first applied and this type was later to be called a 'flashlock'. When a barge required passage downstream the central section would be removed and the flash of water rushing through the lock would 'shoot' the barge over the shallows below it. Such a passage, apart from being dangerous, meant a massive surge of water which swept downstream damaging the river banks and causing local flooding. Modern pound locks have overcome this problem and you will see such a lock later in the walk. There used to be a lock just to the west of Folly Bridge but it was removed in 1884.

Barges would have to pass through weirs constructed by mill-owners to hold back a deep head of water to power their water wheels. The greater the head of water, the more power there was available to the mill. If the mill-owner had to open his weir to allow the passage of a barge it might take several days to recover the lost head of water. The mill-owners therefore made the bargees pay before agreeing to open the weir and, even then, might keep them waiting a day or so while production continued at the mill.

The haphazard construction of weirs and locks in these earlier centuries, and lack of coordination in opening these structures to let floodwaters through, resulted in frequent floods in riverside villages.

Continue across **Folly Bridge**. Cross the road and walk down the sloping footbridge (just past Caudwell's Castle) and continue upstream along the opposite side of the river.

FRIARS WHARF

Look across the river to the housing development which has been built very close to the river.

What action has been taken to reduce the likelihood of these houses being flooded?

Even if flooding from the river was completely prevented, why might these houses still suffer floods?

Building on raised land

Although design features of these houses, such as raised door levels (steps up to the front door) may appear to be included for flood protection, the most important flood protection measure is to ensure that the ground floor of each house lies above the level of the floodplain. Following the disastrous 1947 floods in Oxford, when many residential areas were flooded, the City Council and Thames Conservancy (now Thames Water Authority) decided that if building was to be permitted on the floodplain, it had to be built on land raised by half a metre (18 inches) above that flood level. The extent of the 1947 flood is taken as defining the Thames and Cherwell floodplains, but this now includes additional areas affected by more recent floods, in particular that of December 1979. This planning regulation is applied whenever a request for development is sought, though the authorities, in practice, try to resist any development on the floodplain. If planning permission is granted for development on the floodplain, the authorities attempt to obtain 'floodplain compensation'. This means that since a development reduces the floodplain storage the authorities will look nearby to see whether landscaping, such as lowering a parkland area, can create compensatory floodplain storage.

Even if river flooding could be completely prevented, these houses could still suffer floods because of heavy rainstorms. Drains and storm sewers built to remove surface water from the built-up area have limited capacity. This means that a heavy rainstorm may produce so much runoff that the drains and sewers cannot cope: flooding of the roads results. In addition, if the river level is high then the drains and storm sewers may not be able to pass the runoff into the river : the outlets are effectively blocked. It is possible that 'urban flooding' is on the increase. In some areas, the main drains were built when far fewer buildings existed. Now that many more houses have been added, the result is that there are more occasions when the drains can not cope. Heavy (thunderstorm) rain in Oxford also appears to be on the increase. Whereas a heavy rainstorm, say one which gives 50 mm (two inches) of rainfall in a day, occurred once every twenty years at the turn of the century, it now occurs once every five years!

Continue along the towpath.

River banks and the towpath suffer erosion by the river, leading to slumping. Throughout your walk you may have noticed that the river banks and riverside path are protected from erosion by a variety of methods.

Why do the methods of protection vary from one stretch of the river to another?

This railway bridge originally served the gas works which have now been demolished.

Methods of bank protection

Which method of bank protection is employed depends upon several reasons such as the severity of erosion along each stretch of the river (whether on the inner or outer bend of a meander), the speed with which repairs have to be effected, the cost, the importance of any stretch (such as near buildings and bridges or outlets for drains), and when the protection measures were undertaken (views change as to which method is most effective). Along some stretches of the river, expensive steel sheet piling or stone/concrete blocks have been employed while along other sections hessian sacks filled with a mixture of ballast and cement have been used. These sacks were laid down dry but water from the surrounding land, percolating through the banks into the river, provided the moisture to set the cement. This form of protection lasts about 20 years before having to be replaced. Along other stretches of the river, the river bank is left simply in its natural state.

▼ Flooding of the railway lines near Abingdon Road Bridge in the 19th-century. ◢

Continue along the riverside towpath passing under several bridges. The first railway bridge (with ornate Victorian pierheads) originally served the gas works. Stop at the second railway bridge which carries the main line to London.

RAILWAY BRIDGE

In November 1852, the railway line (the 'permanent way' as it was then called) south of this bridge was flooded. Ballast supporting the railway sleepers was washed away and this led to a railway engine coming off the rails.

What action would you have taken to try to prevent flood damage happening again?

Raising the railway lines

The obvious solution to this flood problem would be to raise the railway lines and, of course, the height of the bridge above the river. Following the November 1852 flooding of the Great Western railway line the company decided to raise the rails by 0.35 metres (14 inches). However, history repeated itself on 15th November 1875, when both lines of rails, still held together by the fastenings of the sleepers, were swept bodily away from their position. Once more the railway lines were raised, only to find that in November 1894 the rail services had to be suspended for seven days because the ballast was washed from beneath the rails. This dramatically highlights the fact that, although one may take action to reduce the likelihood of damage by floods, one cannot be sure that all flood damage will be prevented.

Not only are railway lines raised, as a precaution against flooding, but roads are raised too. The northern by-pass around Oxford has been built well above the floodplain.

A Great Western Railway locomotive attempts to pass through the floodwaters near Abingdon Road Bridge, November 1875.

Continue along the towpath. A footbridge takes you over Bulstake Stream which enters the Thames on your left. Carry on past the monument. Across the river can be seen a private marina which has been built along the former Osney mill stream. Use the footbridge to pass over the Thames and you will come to Osney Lock.

OSNEY LOCK

Although the river needs to be controlled against flooding, it is also an important highway for commercial and pleasure craft. To ensure adequate depth of water throughout the course of the river, many weirs and locks have been built such as this one at Osney. This is a good site for a mill too and, although the last one has now been removed, a mill had existed at this site since the 12th century. The first mill was associated with Osney Abbey, established here in 1129 but dissolved in 1539. Locks are convenient points at which to gauge river levels and rainfall. At each end of the lock can be seen posts which are used to measure the level (stage) of the river above (head water) and below (tail water) the lock. The river levels are automatically measured and this information is sent by telephone-link to the Thames Water Flood Centre at Reading. Information from other locks on the Thames and its tributaries are similarly sent to the Flood Centre and information from each lock is automatically brought up to date every seven minutes. As a check on the accuracy of this information the Flood Centre confirms the levels with each lock-keeper twice a day. The Flood Centre is also sent information on precipitation. Two rain gauges can be seen near the lock-keeper's house. Knowledge of what is happening to the river levels and rainfall throughout the Thames drainage basin allows the Flood Centre to co-ordinate the opening and closing of weir-sluices along the Thames and its tributaries. Such co-ordination ensures that flooding is kept to a minimum. In addition, this information provides the basis for the three-stage flood warning system:

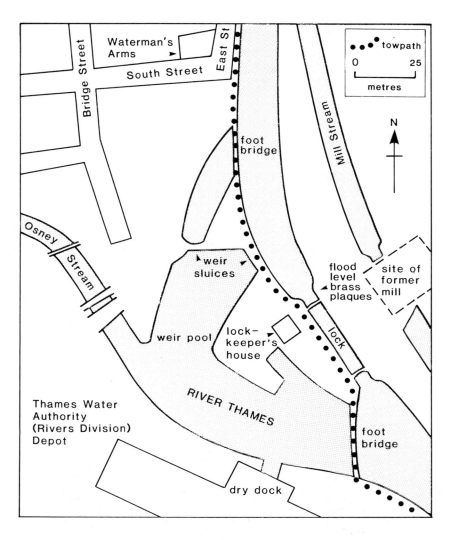

Sketch map showing the area around Osney lock.

- Yellow alert is given when the Thames drainage basin is saturated - that is, at maximum storage - and when any further rain will simply run straight off the land into the river. The yellow alert often operates throughout the whole winter period;

- Amber alert is given when river levels are rising and there is some possibility of flooding in certain areas;

- Red alert is issued when there is danger of serious flooding in low-lying parts along the river.

Thames Water Authority issue these flood alerts to the police and local authorities who, in turn, inform the residents likely to be affected.

If you lived next to the river and received a "red alert' flood warning, and were told your house was likely to flood in a few hours' time, what action would you take?

Plaques marking the two worst floods of the past century, November 1894 and March 1947.

Emergency action

With a possible flood likely in a few hours there is little opportunity to take much more than emergency action. Such action may include:

a. Closing windows and doors. Placing sandbags, or some other form of barrier, across doorways and other openings (such as air bricks) through which water might flow. Thames Water issue sandbags in readiness;

b. Moving possessions upstairs. This is what many people did during the 1947 floods only to suffer additional misery as rain came through roofs which were damaged by the gales of 16th March;

c. Switching off electricity and gas to prevent fire/explosions;

d. Drawing off some clean drinking water;

e. Moving outside possessions such as a car, garden furniture, rabbit hutch, etc. to a safer location;

f. Evacuating the building.

Hopefully, the authorities would provide help and advice. They may also be expected to ensure continued access to flooded homes using duckboards (planks) placed along the sides of the streets. The worst floods here during the past century were in November 1894 and March 1947. These flood levels are clearly marked at the upstream end of the lock by brass plaques. These plaques, it is hoped, lie a considerable height above the present river level! The 1947 floods came when a rapid thaw of deep winter snowfall was accompanied by heavy rainfall onto the frozen ground. Over 3000 homes in Grandpont, Hinksey, Osney, the Friars, Jericho, St.Ebbes and Paradise Square were flooded; some to a depth of one metre (3 feet). The Mayor opened a special relief fund which raised 2,000. This was used to supply disinfectant, coal, soap and other emergency aid to householders. Commenting on this flood at the time, the Thames Conservancy Chief Engineer concluded that the river would have had to have been 'twice as deep and three times as wide' in order to prevent flooding under those conditions. Today the river has been dredged a little deeper, many of the weirs and locks have been rebuilt and modernised, and flood warning systems are more effective, but a flood of similar magnitude is still possible in the future.

Continue along the path, noting the nearby radial and steel buck sluice gates on your left, which are used to control the river level. Pause at the corner of East Street and South Street where the Waterman's Arms public house is located.

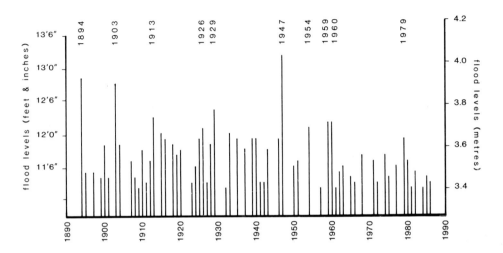

Flood levels (tail water) at Osney lock since the 1890s. Only years in which the level exceeded 3.3 metres (10ft.10ins) are shown. Based on past events, road gullies on Osney Island would be flooded at a level of 3.4 metres, raised planks would be required for access along the streets at 3.5 metres, and houses would be flooded at 3.6 metres. Compare the present tail water level with these levels.

OSNEY ISLAND

Together with West Street, Bridge Street, North Street and Swan Street this residential area is surrounded by watercourses, and it is locally called Osney Island. Osney Island has suffered many floods in the past, with March 1947 being the last major one.

If you had suffered the 1947 flood, but wished to continue living in the same house, what action would you have taken to ensure that you would suffer less in the next major flood?

Flood proofing of homes

There are many actions which you could have taken, given plenty of time and enough money. The City Council may help with some improvements. These include:

a. Concreting the floors. Many of the houses here did this after the 1947 floods. Concreting prevents river water seeping into the house through the river banks, as well as preventing floodwaters from collecting beneath floors, where it is difficult to pump out;

b. Raising the doorstep or placing slots at the entrance to the house into which a board could be fitted when floods threatened. Even the level of windows downstairs could be raised;

c. Insulating the electricity supply to prevent water damage to cables which would otherwise have to be replaced;

d. Ensuring furniture and other fittings could be readily moved upstairs. For example, avoid having fitted carpets;

e. Building a garden wall around the house, if space allows;

f. Taking out insurance;

g. Ensuring that one-way valves are fitted to prevent sewer back-up;

h. Subletting the downstairs rooms to students!

Plus, of course, pressing the authorities to prevent the likelihood of a flood happening at all!

Flooding of South Street and Bridge Street on 21st June 1903. Punts and duckboards ➤ (planks) had to be used for access to homes. ➤

When the river level in the main channel is high, these wooden sluice gates are raised to allow water into Osney Stream.

Continue along East Street, which in places lies below the level of the river. Ahead is Osney Bridge. Stop on the footbridge just before the main road.

OSNEY BRIDGE

From the footbridge you can see below you a sluice gate leading off from the main river channel into a side channel. This side channel, known as Osney Stream, often has very little water in it.

What purpose does the sluice gate and side channel serve?

Flood relief channels

Oxford has many 'flood relief channels' which help to relieve the flood-swollen rivers which pass through the city; this is one of them. When the level of the river Thames is high the sluice gates are opened to take some of the water from the main channel. The water passing into the Osney Stream re-enters the main channel in the large basin near Osney lock. Because of the many relief channels, some visitors have even likened Oxford to Venice! The map shows a number of the important relief streams and ditches. Although these relief channels may not always have water in them, and thus are somewhat unsightly, it is important that they are well-maintained and ready for use.

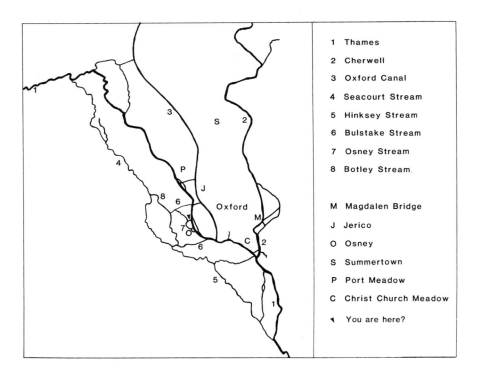

1 Thames
2 Cherwell
3 Oxford Canal
4 Seacourt Stream
5 Hinksey Stream
6 Bulstake Stream
7 Osney Stream
8 Botley Stream.

M Magdalen Bridge
J Jerico
O Osney
S Summertown
P Port Meadow
C Christ Church Meadow
◀ You are here?

Channels which are used to take some of the water from the main channel of the Thames at times of flood.

Cross Osney Bridge. This was built by the Oxford Local Board in 1888 to carry Botley Road and it is the lowest bridge on the Thames. Rejoin the riverside path, which is now on the opposite (eastern) side of the river channel. Continue upstream (northwards) along the path a short distance until you have a good view of the allotments opposite.

OPPOSITE THE ALLOTMENTS

Look across the river to the allotment gardens.

What action has been taken to reduce flooding of the allotments?

Protecting the allotment gardens

Most of the allotment gardens nearest you have been raised slightly. Additionally a great variety of materials has been used to protect the bank from slumping and possible flooding. The allotments on the western side are noticeably lower and are prone to flooding. This flooding occurs, not because the floodwaters overtop the river bank, but because the river water seeps into the banks, passes through the nearside raised allotments and seeps to the surface of these lower allotments. The more astute of the allotment holders on this flood-prone side have made attempts to raise their plots, often at the expense of worsening the floods on their neighbour's allotment!

Flooded Osney allotments, March 1979.

Continue along the towpath. Cross over an arched footbridge and bear left (not right!). On the opposite bank of the main river, where Bulstake Stream leaves the main channel, is the Tumbling Bay Bathing Place. This was originally a men-only bathing station until 1892. Continue north along the path until you reach the lifebuoy station number 52.

OXFORD CITY LIFEBUOY STATION NUMBER 52

Opposite you are extensive fields used for farming. Built-up areas aggravate floods because they have an efficient system of paved surfaces, drains and storm sewers to remove water from the streets as quickly as possible. This results in the water (runoff) reaching the river quickly, rapidly raising the river level and making flooding more likely. In contrast, fields allow rainfall to soak into the soil and the water makes its way to the rivers only slowly. In other words, the rain from, say, a heavy thunderstorm quickly reaches the river if it falls over a built-up area, but takes much longer to reach the river if it falls over open fields. However, some farming practices have led to runoff from fields happening more quickly than when such fields were in their 'natural' state.

What farming practices have led to runoff from fields being much faster than it once was?

Improving field drainage

The fields you see across the other side of the river lie on the floodplain and so they are often flooded and of limited use to the farmer. Farmers have therefore improved their drainage to reduce the time water remains on the land. The duration of grazing is increased but, more importantly, better drainage improves the soil and permits more effective use of fertilisers. This increases the growth of grass and therefore the grazing quality of the land. In addition, the risk of disease to cattle, such as the liver fluke, is reduced.

Land drainage has long been practised. Farmland has been improved by ditching, field-piping and tiling, especially since the 1840s, when cheap machine-made cylindrical tiles became widely available and government grants encouraged their use. Improved drainage has meant faster runoff into the Thames than used to happen with 'natural' fields. Following rainstorms, river levels therefore tend to be higher than they once were, and the likelihood of flooding downstream has increased slightly.

Proceed along the raised path (embankment), which has the river Thames on your left and the Fiddler's Island Stream on your right, until you come to a bridge in about 500 metres. As you walk this stretch of the towpath, note the slumping of the banks in places and the generally less-well-maintained state of the banks now you have left the built-up area of Oxford. At times of even low floods, this path would appear to need further raising for it to be of use.

FIDDLER'S ISLAND BRIDGE AND PORT MEADOW

Standing on the bridge gives you a good view of Port Meadow. This is an extensive area of low-lying grassland on which many horses and cattle graze. This area is frequently flooded and in winter the frozen shallow water makes it ideal for skating. Land at the southern end of the meadow, is noticeably higher than the rest of the meadow, as it was raised in the late 19th-century using waste and refuse from Oxford. Today, this raised land provides a sanctuary from floodwaters for the Port Meadow animals.

Why is it important not to raise any more land in Port Meadow?

◄ ◄ A tranquil day on Port Meadow during the floods of 1875.

Preserving Port Meadow in its natural state

The reason for not raising any more land in Port Meadow, so permitting it to flood, is primarily that it is part of the floodplain of the river Thames. Preservation of an unspoilt or natural landscape may also be important: raising the land would change the nature of the meadow.

A floodplain serves an important function in slowing down the flow of large floods, spreading their effects by avoiding a concentration of floodwater and providing a greater capacity channel. Any reduction in the area into which the river may flood here, would mean that floodwaters would be passed further downstream, raising the river level there, and making floods worse in Oxford itself. This is why since 1974 the Thames Water Authority and the Oxford City Council have resisted further development of any of the floodplain for, say, housing.

Flooding of fields surrounding Oxford, 1929.

This is the end of the trail. You now have a choice. You can either cross the bridge (to your right) into Port Meadow returning to the centre of Oxford from the north (via Jericho), or you may decide to return to Osney Bridge, returning to the centre of Oxford from the west. Whichever you choose, you may wish to extend your walk by crossing the Thames (over the bridge to your left), and continuing for another 800 metres to the 17th-century public house, The Perch, at Binsey.

Acknowledgements:

Many people have helped in the preparation of this trail by walking it and commenting on early drafts. In particular, the author wishes to thank Peter and Janet Keene of Thematic Trails; Heather Jones and David Pepper of the Geography Section, Oxford Polytechnic; numerous students from Oxford Polytechnic and Cheney School; Dennis Boreham and Mel Slingo of Thames Water Flood Centre at Reading; several staff from Thames Water Rivers Division including Mr N.N.Pyke, a former Area Engineer based at Osney; and the Osney lock-keeper. The diagrams were drawn by Heather Jones and the sketches by Elizabeth Elsom. Several of the photographs and engravings are reproduced by kind permission of the Oxford City Library, the Oxford University Bodleian Library and Aerofilms Limited.

Published by Thematic Trails, Geography Section, Oxford Polytechnic, Oxford OX3 0BP

Typeset on a Lasercomp at Oxford University Computing Service

Printed in Great Britain by Witney Press, Oxfordshire

As you walk back into Oxford, consider the wide range of flood protection measures adopted along the route you have walked. The measures fall into two categories:

1. Action associated with the river channel;

a. Widening and deepening the channel by dredging;
b. Stabilising the river banks using steel sheet piling, stone/concrete blocks, cement bags, etc.;
c. Straightening the channel;
d. Ensuring where a tributary joins the main channel its waters do not oppose the flow in the main channel;
e. Building earth or concrete embankments or walls alongside the channel;
f. Replacing bridges which have massive piers and narrow arches; widening bridge spans;
g. Widening locks and lowering their sills (bases);
h. Ensuring the operation of weir-sluices is co-ordinated by the Thames Water Flood Centre; ensuring all locks are fully opened during floods;
i. Creating additional river channels (relief channels);
j. Keeping the river channel, and relief channels, free of debris (branches, weeds, rubbish) which may lead to blockages.

2. Action on the floodplain.

a. Providing flood alerts so residents can undertake emergency action such as sandbagging of doorways, evacuation, etc.
b. Ensuring buildings incorporate flood-proofing measures such as concrete floors, insulation of the electricity supply, raised doorsteps, etc.
c. Ensuring if development has to take place, the land is raised above the height of a major flood;
d. Discouraging further building on the floodplain; transforming derelict urban sites into parkland or recreation fields;
e. Lowering parkland or recreation areas within the floodplain, to increase the storage of water during floods;
f. Encouraging floodplain residents to have adequate insurance cover against flooding.

There is a third group of actions that can be taken to reduce the flood problem and this refers to actions taken anywhere in the river drainage basin (catchment). As explained earlier, the speed with which runoff from the land reaches the river channel determines how quickly the river level will rise. If, after a heavy rainstorm, runoff from the whole of the basin reaches the river very quickly then the river level may reach flood level. Actions which slow down the speed with which runoff reaches the river can be undertaken in the river basin. For example, runoff from built-up areas reaches the river very quickly but runoff from grassland areas is much slower while runoff from forested areas is even slower still. In other words, the introduction of forested areas in a river basin would help reduce the flood problem. Similarly, the creation of more grassland and wooded areas in built-up areas would help.

Another flood protection measure which could be taken would be to build a flood storage reservoir. When river levels were rising, some of the water could be taken out of the river and stored temporarily in a reservoir. However, few of this type of reservoir have been built in this country. Farmoor reservoir, upstream from Oxford, was built to provide the drinking water supply for the city and not for flood storage. The two purposes are incompatible given the dirty nature of floodwaters. For example, floodwaters may contain a high concentration of nitrates, washed from fields onto which fertilisers have been added, and it is difficult and expensive to purify such water for drinking purposes.

STUDENTS AND TEACHERS

Teachers wishing to use the walk as a trail may obtain a workbook version suitable for photocopying for groups from, Peter Keene (Editor), Thematic Trails, Geography Section, Oxford Polytechnic, Oxford OX3 0BP. The workbooks include directions, questions and spaces for answers, but exclude observations and discussion. This enables the leader to offer explanation at a level appropriate to the group's needs, or alternatively to defer discussion until completion of the walk. The workbook is therefore suitable for a wide range of ages and ability. Permission need not be sought to reproduce these workbook versions of the walk provided that copies are made only in the educational establishment which uses them, and that such copies are not sold, hired or lent to any other individual, organisation or establishment.

This is one of a series of walks published by Thematic Trails. each develops a particular theme and it is the intention that by the end of the walk each theme will have been sufficiently developed to enable the participant to transfer this knowledge to the interpretation of similar environments elsewhere.

These walks are being published in district sets and include themes associated with ecology, geology, geography, history, art and architecture. The districts being developed initially are the Oxford Region, North Devon and South Devon. Further details may be obtained from the editor.

Walks   available   from   Thematic   Trails

OXFORD REGION

Taming the Rivers of Oxford; a riverside walk. Derek M Elsom (1987)
Geology and the Building of Oxford. Paul Jenkins *
Changeless Oxfordshire Villages? John Brooks *
Architectural Change in Central Oxford. Jeanne Sheehy *
A Walk on the Wild Side; ecology in the city of Oxford. Janet Keene *

NORTH DEVON

Westward Ho! Ecology Trail; beach, sand-dune, salt-marsh. Janet Keene (1985)
Across the Rocky Shore at Westward Ho! Janet Keene (1985)
Westward Ho! man against the sea. Peter Keene (1986)
Westward Ho! Coastal Landscape Trail. Peter Keene (1986)
Braunton Burrows Ecology Trail. Janet Keene (1987)
Geology at Hartland Quay. Alan Childs & Chris Cornford *
Hartland Quay Coastal Landscape; a cliff walk. Peter Keene *
Strawberry Water to Marsland Mouth; a coastal walk. Peter Keene *
Coastal Landscape Walks at Saunton and Baggy. Chris Cornford & Peter Keene *
Lynton Valley of Rocks; a landscape walk *
The Art of Clovelly; a village walk. John Bradbeer *
Bideford Town; a history walk. Peter Christie *
Barnstaple; a town walk. John Bradbeer *

SOUTH DEVON

Prawle Peninsula Landscape Trail. Phil Harvey & Peter Keene
[Field Studies Council] (1986)
Burrator; Dartmoor landform trail. Peter Keene
[Nature Conservancy Council] *
Dawlish Warren Coastal Management Trail. Peter Sims *

SLIDE SET

Taming the Rivers of Oxford Slides. Derek M. Elsom (1987).
Thematic Trails, Oxford Polytechnic. A set of 24 slides with notes, illustrating some of
the links which have developed between the rivers, the people and the city of Oxford.

Details from:
Peter Keene (Editor), Thematic Trails,
Oxford Polytechnic, Oxford OX3 0BP   [* In preparation 1987]